THE ULTIMATE
NEWCASTLE UNITED
TRIVIA BOOK

A Collection of Amazing Trivia Quizzes
and Fun Facts for Die-Hard Magpies Fans!

Ray Walker

Exclusive Free Book
Crazy Sports Stories

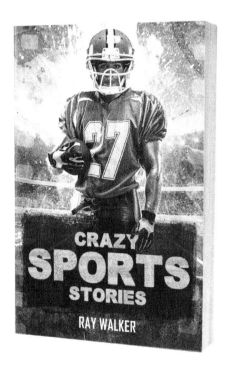

As a thank you for getting a copy of this book I would like to offer you a free copy of my book Crazy Sports Stories which comes packed with interesting stories from your favorite sports such as Football, Hockey, Baseball, Basketball and more.

Grab your free copy over at
RayWalkerMedia.com/Bonus

CONTENTS

INTRODUCTION

The seeds for Newcastle United were planted back in the late 1870s and early 1880s and began to grow roots with several local soccer clubs. When the city's East and West End teams merged in 1892, Newcastle United was born. Since then, they've been entertaining fans in the North East of England and all over the nation by winning several league and FA Cup championships.

With the team being nicknamed the "Magpies" and its fans being known as the "Toon Army," the club's history is certainly very colorful and entertaining. The side may not be the strongest and most successful in the country, but it's always been one of the most intriguing, with its fans supporting the club through thick and thin.

Newcastle is well known for its fighting spirit, and when the team did suffer through relegations, it quickly battled back to earn promotion shortly afterward in most cases. In fact, the club has never played below the second tier in the English Football League.

The side has also tried its luck in Europe and won a few minor titles, such as the Anglo-Italian Cup and Texaco Cup, with its biggest triumph being the European (Inter-Cities)

Fairs Cup in 1969. European Champions League and Europa League success has been hard to come by, and the team is still searching for its first domestic League Cup, but it hasn't been due to lack of effort.

Newcastle supporters have been treated to some of the world's best players and managers over the years, with some of the most memorable being Kevin Keegan, Paul Gascoigne, Les Ferdinand, Shay Given, Joe Harvey, Rob Lee, Jimmy Lawrence, Bobby Moncur, Colin Veitch, Glenn Roeder, Andy Cole, Nolberto Solano, Alan Shearer, and Sir Bobby Robson.

This trivia and fact book has been written to celebrate the intriguing history of Newcastle United because there's never a dull moment around St. James' Park. There have been turbulent times and periods of euphoria. Our goal is to present the highs with the lows. You'll be able to read about the club's greatest members and how each one of them influenced the side.

Newcastle's story is covered here in an entertaining quiz form with 12 unique chapters each representing a different topic. All sections come with 20 stimulating quiz questions along with 10 educational "Did You Know?" facts. The quizzes are presented in multiple-choice and true-false options with the answers on a separate page.

Reading this book is an ideal way to challenge yourself and others about the remarkable history of Newcastle United. You'll be well prepared to take on all challenges when it comes to quiz showdowns and also spread the word about your favorite club at the same time.

CHAPTER 1:

ORIGINS & HISTORY

QUIZ TIME!

1. What year was Newcastle United FC founded?

    a. 1899

    b. 1892

    c. 1886

    d. 1880

2. Newcastle was formed when two clubs, Newcastle East End and Newcastle West End, merged.

    a. True

    b. False

3. Which league did Newcastle originally play in?

    a. The Combination League

    b. The Football Alliance

    c. The Northern League

    d. Football League

4. The club played its first match at St. James' Park against which club?

a. Middlesbrough Ironopolis FC

b. Glasgow Celtic

c. Sunderland AFC

d. Corinthian FC

5. What was the club's original crest design?

a. A boat on the River Tyne

b. A lion holding a sword

c. A magpie

d. Newcastle upon Tyne's coat of arms

6. What was the outcome of the team's first match at St. James' Park?

a. draw

b. win

c. 2-2 draw

d. loss

7. The team has played its home games at St. James' Park since the club was founded.

a. True

b. False

8. What is the team's nickname?

a. The Seahorses

b. The Magpies

c. The United

d. The River

9. How many different official crests has Newcastle used as of 2020?

a. 9

b. 6

c. 4

d. 2

10. The side played its first Northern League match against which club?

    a. Stockton FC

    b. Middlesbrough FC

    c. Darlington FC

    d. Sheffield United

11. What was the outcome of the squad's first Northern League match?

    a. 5-1 loss

    b. 4-4 draw

    c. 3-0 win

    d. 2-2 draw

12. Newcastle has never been relegated from the Premier League as of 2020.

    a. True

    b. False

13. What was the team's original shirt color?

    a. Blue

    b. Red

    c. White

    d. Green

14. How many times has Newcastle been relegated as of 2020?

    a. 2
    b. 4
    c. 6
    d. 7

15. What team did Newcastle face in its first Premier League game?

    a. Tottenham Hotspur
    b. Swindon Town FC
    c. Coventry City FC
    d. Manchester United

16. Newcastle was accepted into the First Division of the Football League on its second application.

    a. True
    b. False

17. Which club did Newcastle play in its first match in the Football League?

    a. Ardwick FC
    b. Small Heath
    c. Notts County FC
    d. Woolwich Arsenal

18. Against which club did Newcastle win its first Premier League match?

    a. Oldham Athletic
    b. Blackburn Rovers

c. Everton FC

d. Aston Villa

19. What was the outcome of the club's first match in the Football League?

    a. 6-0 win

    b. 2-2 draw

    c. 3-1 loss

    d. 3-2 win

20. Newcastle's final game of the 2002-03 season was delayed 45 minutes because the team arrived late.

    a. True

    b. False

QUIZ ANSWERS

1. B – 1892

2. A – True

3. C – The Northern League

4. B – Glasgow Celtic

5. D – Newcastle upon Tyne's coat of arms

6. D – 1-0 loss

7. A – True

8. B – The Magpies

9. C – 4

10. D – Sheffield United

11. A – 5-1 loss

12. B – False

13. B – Red

14. C – 6

15. A – Tottenham Hotspur

16. B – False

17. D – Woolwich Arsenal

18. C – Everton FC

19. B – 2-2 draw

20. B – False

DID YOU KNOW?

1. Newcastle United FC was formed in the summer of 1892 when the Newcastle East End club absorbed the assets of city rivals Newcastle West End. This merger also included the lease of St. James' Park, and a new name, Newcastle United, was created to signify the unification of the clubs. The name was officially recognized on December 9, 1892.

2. The first recorded soccer game in the Newcastle area took place in 1877, with the region's first club, Tyne Association. The Newcastle Rangers club was formed the following year. However, the roots of Newcastle United can be traced to two minor soccer clubs in the city's east end, named Stanley and Rosewood. Stanley was formed in 1881 originally as a cricket club and changed its name to Newcastle East End in October 1882.

3. Rosewood was formed just before Stanley and joined with Newcastle East End to form a stronger unit. At the same time, a new organization, the West End Football Club, was formed; in 1886, it took over the lease of a soccer ground at St. James' Park. The English Football League kicked off in 1888, but the Newcastle area clubs formed a local league in 1889-90 named the Northern League, consisting of 10 founding teams that were a mixture of amateur and professional outfits.

4. Both the Newcastle West End and East End clubs became limited companies in 1890 and began to sell shares as a way to attract better players by paying them more. However, Newcastle wasn't really big enough to support two clubs at the time, and the West End team came near to bankruptcy in 1891-92. The club then offered its St. James' Park lease to their East End rivals. In May 1892, East End agreed to take over the lease, along with West End's assets and some of its players.

5. Still named Newcastle East End, the club's first match at St. James' Park came against Glasgow Celtic on September 3, 1892, with the visitors winning the friendly 1-0 in front of 6,000 fans. A meeting was held on December 9, 1892, at Bath Lane Hall, where Newcastle East End changed its name to Newcastle United. The legal title of the club wasn't changed, though, until Newcastle United was set up as a private company limited by shares in September 1895.

6. The club attempted to join the First Division of the Football League in 1893 but was turned down and offered a spot in the Second Division instead. It accepted the invitation, along with Arsenal and Liverpool. At the time, the East End kit color was red, and in 1894, it was changed to the black-and-white stripes the team still plays in at home, along with black shorts and black socks.

7. In 1898, the club earned promotion to the First Division following a series of test matches that were an early version of modern-era playoff games. The first league title

was won in 1904-05, with the club's first FA Cup success being in 1909-10 after losing the final in 1904-05, 1905-06, and 1907-08. As of 2020-21, the club was playing in the top-flight English Premier League. The team's nickname is the Magpies, and its fans are referred to as the Toon Army and the Geordies.

8. The club has been a member of the Premier League for all but three years of the competition's history since it played its inaugural season in 1992-93. As of 2020-21, the team has never played below the second tier in the English soccer league system. The most successful period for the team came from 1904 to 1910 when it captured one FA Cup and three First Division titles.

9. Newcastle operates a youth academy and a Newcastle United FC Reserves team with the Under-23 squad playing its home games at Whitley Park or St. James' Park. The Under-18 side plays its home matches at the academy base at Little Benton, which is part of Newcastle United's Darsley Park training ground.

10. Newcastle United Women is a women's soccer club that is affiliated with Newcastle United FC. It was founded in 1989 and based at the Newcastle United Academy Training Centre. The team plays its home matches at Druid Park, Woolsington, where they competed in the FA Women's National League Division One North in 2020-21. The club became officially affiliated with Newcastle United in 2016 and is nicknamed The Lady Magpies.

CHAPTER 2:

THE CAPTAIN CLASS

QUIZ TIME!

1. Which captain later managed the club between 2006 and 2007?

   a. Kevin Keegan
   b. Rob Lee
   c. Mick Martin
   d. Glenn Roeder

2. Newcastle named 14 different full-time skippers between 2010 and 2020.

   a. True
   b. False

3. Who was appointed Newcastle skipper in 2016?

   a. Karl Darlow
   b. Curtis Good
   c. Jamaal Lascelles
   d. Callum Roberts

4. Glenn Roeder captained which club before joining the Magpies?

   a. Sheffield United
   b. Watford FC
   c. Queens Park Rangers
   d. Leyton Orient FC

5. Who captained the side to FA Cup titles in 1951 and 1952?

   a. Tommy Walker
   b. Bobby Cowell
   c. Ronnie Simpson
   d. Joe Harvey

6. Which player was stripped of the armband by manager Ruud Gullit?

   a. Barry Venison
   b. Andy Thorn
   c. Rob Lee
   d. Brian Kilcline

7. Colin Veitch captained Newcastle to seven FA Cup finals.

   a. True
   b. False

8. Who did Alan Shearer replace as skipper in 1998?

   a. Rob Lee
   b. Peter Beardsley
   c. Ian Rush
   d. Andy Griffin

9. Which club did Barry Venison captain before coming to Newcastle?

 a. Preston North End
 b. Liverpool FC
 c. Southampton FC
 d. Sunderland AFC

10. Glenn Roeder succeeded which player as captain?

 a. Mick Martin
 b. Kevin Keegan
 c. Andy Thorn
 d. Terry McDermott

11. Which club did Kevin Nolan captain after leaving Newcastle?

 a. Bolton Wanderers
 b. Leyton Orient FC
 c. West Ham United
 d. Notts County FC

12. Joe Beardsley captained Newcastle for 10 seasons.

 a. True
 b. False

13. Who succeeded Roy Aitken as captain?

 a. Kevin Scott
 b. Andy Thorn
 c. Brian Kilcline
 d. Terry Hibbitt

14. Brian Kilcline captained which club before joining Newcastle?

   a. West Ham United
   b. Swindon Town FC
   c. Oldham Athletic
   d. Coventry City FC

15. Which player captained the club to its last FA Cup victory in 1954-55?

   a. Geoff Nulty
   b. Bobby Moncur
   c. Joe Harvey
   d. Jimmy Scoular

16. In addition to captaining Newcastle, Andy Aitken skippered the Scottish national team for 10 matches.

   a. True
   b. False

17. Who did Jamaal Lascelles succeed as captain?

   a. Kevin Nolan
   b. Fabricio Coloccini
   c. Alan Smith
   d. Tim Krul

18. Roy Aitken captained which side before signing with Newcastle?

   a. Celtic FC
   b. Aberdeen FC
   c. St. Mirren FC
   d. Fulham FC

19. Which player succeeded Geoff Nulty as captain?

   a. Irving Nattrass
   b. Kevin Keegan
   c. Mick Martin
   d. Terry Hibbitt

20. When Kevin Keegan took over as manager, he handed the armband to Michael Owen in 2008.

   a. True
   b. False

QUIZ ANSWERS

1. D – Glenn Roeder

2. B – False

3. C – Jamaal Lascelles

4. C – Queens Park Rangers

5. D – Joe Harvey

6. C – Rob Lee

7. B – False

8. A – Rob Lee

9. D – Sunderland AFC

10. B – Kevin Keegan

11. C – West Ham United

12. B – False

13. A – Kevin Scott

14. D – Coventry City FC

15. D – Jimmy Scoular

16. B – False

17. B – Fabricio Coloccini

18. A – Celtic FC

19. D – Terry Hibbitt

20. A – True

DID YOU KNOW?

1. Scottish international defender Bob "Bobby" Moncur wore the armband between 1968 and 1974 after making his Second Division debut as an 18-year-old in 1963. Moncur aided his teammates in winning the European (Inter-Cities) Fairs Cup in 1968-69 and the 1973-74 FA Cup final against Liverpool, where they were beaten 3-0. That was his last of over 350 games for the team. He then joined Sunderland. Moncur became a manager, television pundit, and a Magpies ambassador after hanging up his boots.

2. Bill McCracken was one of the club's longest-serving players as he played 432 times between 1904 and 1923. The colorful Irish international was a superb defender who joined from Distillery in his homeland and was a favorite of St. James' Park fans. McCracken was one of the team's and his country's earliest captains. He helped the club hoist three First Division titles and reach three FA Cup finals, winning one in 1909-10. He would have played dozens of more games if it hadn't been for World War I. McCracken later became a scout for Newcastle and is in the club's Hall of Fame.

3. Another early Newcastle skipper and club Hall-of-Famer was defender Colin Veitch. The English international played his entire pro career with his hometown team

from 1899 to 1914. He could play anywhere on the pitch but was usually found in midfield or defense. He was a cornerstone of the squad with 49 goals in 322 contests and helped his teammates win the 1909-10 FA Cup as well as three First Division titles. Veitch was also a scholar, actor, musician, and playwright who helped found Newcastle's People's Theatre.

4. Glenn Roeder managed Newcastle between 2006 and 2007 and played with the side from 1983 to 1989 while wearing the armband between 1984 and 1988. He arrived from Queens Park Rangers, where he was team captain, in December 1983 for a reported fee of £125,000. The defender played over 200 games with the Magpies and helped them earn promotion from the Second Division in 1983-84. He left for Watford on a free transfer and hung up his boots in 1993 while with Gillingham as a player-manager. Sadly, Roeder passed away at the age of 65 on February 18, 2021.

5. English international Rob Lee arrived from Charlton for a reported £700,000 in 1992 and stayed for a decade while playing nearly 400 games and scoring over 50 goals. The team won the second-tier First Division in his first season to earn promotion to the newly formed Premier League, with Lee contributing 10 goals in 36 matches. He was named to the PFA Premier League Team of the Year for 1995-96 and appointed captain in 1997. However, Ruud Gullit took over as manager in 1998 and took the armband away soon after. Lee was then sold to Derby County for a

reported £250,000. He is a member of the Newcastle United Hall of Fame.

6. As of March 2021, the club skipper was Jamaal Lascelles. He was given the armband in August 2016 by manager Rafael Benítez, who liked the player's willingness to speak up in the team's dressing room. Lascelles arrived in 2014 from Nottingham Forest with Karl Darlow, but both players were loaned back to Forest for the 2014-15 campaign. Newcastle was relegated from the Premier League in 2015-16 with Lascelles leading the team back to the top flight by winning the Championship League title in 2016-17 when he was named to the PFA Championship Team of the Year. Lascelles was closing in on 200 appearances for the club in 2021 and had chipped in with 10 goals.

7. Wearing the armband from 1979 to 1982 was Republic of Ireland international midfielder Mick Martin. He joined the side in 1978 from West Bromwich Albion for a reported £100,000 and played just over 160 games before leaving to play in Canada in 1984. After hanging up his boots in 1987, Martin returned to the Magpies for a stint on the coaching staff and then turned to broadcasting. His father Con Martin was an Irish international and played for Aston Villa, while his brother Con Martin Jr. and nephew Owen Garvan also played pro soccer.

8. Argentine international defender Fabricio Coloccini was one of the few Newcastle players to wear the armband who was born outside of the British Isles. He arrived in

August 2008 from Deportivo La Coruña for approximately £10.3 million and was promoted to skipper in July 2011. He wore the armband before returning to Argentina to play with San Lorenzo in July 2016. He played 275 times with the Magpies and helped the side take the 2009-10 Championship League title while being named to the PFA Team of the Year. He was named to the 2011-12 Premier League Team of the Year.

9. Cameroon international defender/midfielder Geremi Sorele Njitap Fotso, known simply as Geremi, wore the armband with Newcastle only for a brief time. He joined in July 2007 from Chelsea and was appointed skipper by manager Sam Allardyce. However, when Kevin Keegan took over as boss, he handed the captaincy to Michael Owen in January 2008. Geremi played just over 50 games before joining Turkish club MKE Ankaragücü in February 2010. However, he helped the Magpies win the 2009-10 Championship League title before leaving.

10. The appointed team captain for the 1991-92 campaign was defender Kevin Scott, who had started his pro career with the club in 1984 after joining as a youth and winning the FA Youth Cup in 1985. He played just over 225 times with the side before joining Tottenham Hotspur in 1994. He helped his teammates to the Second Division title in 1992-93 before being transferred for a reported £850,000. After retiring in 2000, Scott worked as a coach with the Middlesbrough FC academy and then tried his hand as a driving instructor.

CHAPTER 3:

AMAZING MANAGERS

QUIZ TIME!

1. Who is recognized as the club's first official full-time manager?

    a. Frank Watt

    b. Andy Cunningham

    c. Tom Mather

    d. Stan Seymour

2. Until 1929, Newcastle team selection was run by a committee.

    a. True

    b. False

3. Ruud Gullit was the player-manager of which club before joining the Magpies?

    a. Feyenoord

    b. PSV Eindhoven

    c. AC Milan

    d. Chelsea FC

4. Who managed the team to the 1968-69 European (Inter-Cities) Fairs Cup?

    a. Bobby Robson
    b. Stan Seymour
    c. Kevin Keegan
    d. Joe Harvey

5. Who did Steve Bruce succeed as manager in July 2019?

    a. Chris Hughton
    b. Rafael Benítez
    c. Steve McClaren
    d. Alan Pardew

6. Who was the club's first manager born outside the British Isles?

    a. Carlo Ancelotti
    b. Rafael Benítez
    c. Osvaldo Ardiles
    d. Ruud Gullit

7. Newcastle has had 48 full-time managers as of 2020.

    a. True
    b. False

8. Which club did Rafael Benítez join Newcastle from?

    a. Real Madrid
    b. Valencia CF
    c. S.S.C. Napoli
    d. Chelsea FC

9. Who was the club's longest-serving manager in total as of 2020?

   a. Stan Seymour
   b. Joe Harvey
   c. Kevin Keegan
   d. Arthur Cox

10. Alan Pardew managed which club after leaving Newcastle?

    a. West Ham United
    b. Crystal Palace
    c. Southampton FC
    d. Charlton Athletic

11. How many stints as manager did Stan Seymour serve?

    a. 1
    b. 2
    c. 3
    d. 4

12. Kevin Keegan had three stints as Newcastle's manager.

    a. True
    b. False

13. Steve Bruce resigned from which club immediately before joining the Magpies?

    a. Wigan Athletic
    b. Sheffield United
    c. Huddersfield Town
    d. Sheffield Wednesday

14. Which manager did Alan Pardew succeed in December 2010?

    a. Alan Shearer
    b. Chris Hughton
    c. Joe Kinnear
    d. John Carver

15. Who managed Newcastle in its first season in the Premier League?

    a. Osvaldo Ardiles
    b. Kevin Keegan
    c. Bobby Saxton
    d. Kenny Dalglish

16. Newcastle has had 15 caretaker managers as of 2020.

    a. True
    b. False

17. Who succeeded Kenny Dalglish as boss in August 1998?

    a. Glenn Roeder
    b. Graeme Souness
    c. Ruud Gullit
    d. Bobby Robson

18. Arthur Cox managed which club before he managed Newcastle?

    a. Chesterfield FC
    b. Derby County FC
    c. Fulham FC
    d. Brighton & Hove Albion FC

19. Which club did Kenny Dalglish manage from 1991 to 1995 before joining Newcastle?

    a. Blackburn Rovers

    b. West Bromwich Albion

    c. Tottenham Hotspur

    d. Celtic FC

20. Joe Harvey won over 250 games with Newcastle as manager.

    a. True

    b. False

QUIZ ANSWERS

1. B – Andy Cunningham
2. A – True
3. D – Chelsea FC
4. D – Joe Harvey
5. B – Rafael Benítez
6. C – Osvaldo Ardiles
7. B – False
8. A – Real Madrid
9. A – Stan Seymour
10. B – Crystal Palace
11. C – 3
12. B – False
13. D – Sheffield Wednesday
14. B – Chris Hughton
15. B – Kevin Keegan
16. B – False
17. C – Ruud Gullit
18. A – Chesterfield FC
19. A – Blackburn Rovers
20. B – False

DID YOU KNOW?

1. There have been just over 30 official managers at Newcastle since 1930. The current boss, as of March 2021, Steve Bruce, was appointed in July 2019. Chris Hughton posted the side's best winning percentage at 59.38 as a full-time manager, while Stan Seymour was the longest-serving manager with three stints between 1939 and 1958. Joe Harvey enjoyed the longest consecutive spell at 13 years, from 1962 to 1975. The only three managers who never guided the club in the top flight were Tom Mather, Norman Smith, and Osvaldo Ardiles.

2. The club's team was selected by a committee from 1892 to 1929 with a secretary in place instead of an official manager. Newcastle's first secretary was Frank Watt, who was reportedly appointed to the position in 1895. The team was successful under Watt as it won four First Division titles and three Northern League championships and reached the FA Cup final five times, winning one of them.

3. Andy Cunningham is regarded as the club's first official manager. He took the post in 1930, while Frank Watt remained its secretary until 1935. Cunningham started with the side as a player, then became player-manager and finally the full-time manager. He helped the squad hoist the FA Cup in 1931-32, but in 1933-34, they were

relegated to the Second Division. Cunningham was replaced in the summer of 1935 by Tom Mather.

4. In September 1939, former Magpies player Stan Seymour was appointed manager and held the job until the spring of 1947 when he stepped down in favor of George Martin. However, Seymour was back in the driver's seat in December 1950 when Martin joined Aston Villa. He then guided the side to FA Cup trophies in 1950-51 and 1951-52. This achievement meant Seymour became the first person in England to win the FA Cup with the same club as both a player and manager. He stepped down in 1954, and Doug Livingstone became the next manager.

5. Doug Livingstone's reign as manager lasted until January 1956, and, even though he was officially in charge when the club won the 1954-55 FA Cup, he was involved in a power struggle with the board of directors. He then resigned, and Stan Seymour took over as manager for the third time in January 1956. The team struggled, though, and Seymour's final stint as boss ended in June 1958 when Charlie Mitten took over. Seymour remained on the club's board and was appointed Life President in 1976. He passed away in 1978. His son, Stan Seymour Jr., later became chairman of the club.

6. Joe Harvey was manager from June 1962 to June 1975 after leading the squad to FA Cup titles in 1951 and 1952 as the team's captain. He led the team to the Second Division title in 1964-65 and won the European (Inter-

Cities) Fairs Cup final in 1968-69 for the club's first taste of continental success. He was also at the helm when the side won the Anglo-Italian Cup in 1973 and the Texaco Cup in 1974 and 1975 before resigning in June 1975 when he was replaced by Gordon Lee. Harvey also took over as caretaker manager for a few games in August 1980 before Arthur Cox was appointed.

7. Former playing great Osvaldo Ardiles of Argentina became Newcastle's first manager born outside of the British Isles when he was appointed in March 1991. His team finished the 1990-91 season in 11th place in the Second Division but struggled the following campaign and found itself in a relegation battle. With Newcastle in danger of dropping down to the third tier of English soccer for the first time, Ardiles was replaced by Kevin Keegan in February 1992. Keegan managed to keep the team in the Second Division with a 2-1 victory over Leicester City on the final day of the season.

8. The second foreign-born manager at Newcastle was former Dutch international player Ruud Gullit, who took over in August 1998 after leaving Chelsea, where he was player-manager. Gullit didn't get along with striker Alan Shearer and stripped the captaincy from Robert Lee while making him train with the reserves. Newcastle finished the season in 13th place but reached the FA Cup final against Manchester United. Gullit began the 1999-2000 campaign with Newcastle but benched Shearer and Duncan Ferguson in a Tyne-Wear Derby against Sunderland which

resulted in a 2-1 defeat. Gullit resigned after this match just a few games into the season.

9. When Ruud Gullit resigned as manager in August 1998, Steve Clarke took over as caretaker for two games until Bobby Robson was hired. Robson had already managed seven teams including England, PSV Eindhoven, Sporting Lisbon, Porto, and Barcelona. He managed the side in the 2001 UEFA Intertoto Cup to a co-finalist spot where they were beaten on the away goals rule. Robson guided the team to a European Champions League berth and the semifinals of the UEFA Cup. However, he was fired in 2004 and retired from managing, being replaced by Graeme Souness. Robson was knighted in 2002 and became Sir Robert William Robson.

10. Former Republic of Ireland international Chris Hughton had stints as caretaker manager in 2008 and 2009 and was named full-time boss in October 2009. He led the team to the second-tier Championship League division with 102 points in 2009-10 as the club broke the 100-point barrier for the first time. However, the team struggled in the Premier League at the start of 2010-11, and Hughton was fired on December 6, 2010, to be replaced with Alan Pardew. As full-time boss, Hughton won 38 games, drew 11, and lost 15 for a club-high 59.38 winning percentage for a permanent manager.

CHAPTER 4:

GOALTENDING GREATS

QUIZ TIME!

1. Who played between the posts in Newcastle's first Premier League match?

    a. Shaka Hislop
    b. Tommy Wright
    c. Pavel Srníček
    d. Mike Hooper

2. Shay Given won the FWA Footballer of the Year award in 1999-2000.

    a. True
    b. False

3. Which player has made the most all-time appearances for Newcastle in all competitions?

    a. Willie McFaul
    b. Ronnie Simpson
    c. Shay Given
    d. Jimmy Lawrence

4. Who backed up Rob Elliot in nine matches in the 2015-16 Premier League?

   a. Jak Alnwick
   b. Tim Krul
   c. Matz Sels
   d. Karl Darlow

5. How many clean sheets did Tim Krul keep in the 2014-15 domestic league?

   a. 15
   b. 13
   c. 10
   d. 8

6. Which player recorded 21 clean sheets in the 2009-10 domestic league?

   a. Tim Krul
   b. Matt Thomas
   c. Steve Harper
   d. Rob Elliot

7. Shay Given won the Premier League Golden Glove award in 2005-06.

   a. True
   b. False

8. How many appearances did Shay Given make in all competitions for the Magpies?

   a. 381
   b. 394

c. 438

d. 462

9. Who kept four clean sheets in the 2017-18 domestic league?

    a. Karl Darlow

    b. Martin Dúbravka

    c. Rob Elliot

    d. Matz Sels

10. How many clean sheets did Shaka Hislop post in the 1995-96 Premier League?

    a. 13

    b. 11

    c. 8

    d. 5

11. Which player backed up Shay Given for 18 matches in the 2006-07 Premier League season?

    a. Steve Harper

    b. Pavel Srníček

    c. Eddie Edgar

    d. Gary Kelly

12. Martin Dúbravka appeared in every domestic league game in 2018-19.

    a. True

    b. False

13. How many appearances did Jimmy Lawrence make in all competitions?

a. 452

b. 467

c. 496

d. 514

14. Which club did Steve Harper leave Newcastle for?

a. Brighton & Hove Albion

b. Huddersfield Town FC

c. Sunderland AFC

d. Hull City FC

15. How many clean sheets did Shay Given keep in all competitions with Newcastle?

a. 92

b. 89

c. 76

d. 65

16. Tim Krul made 13 appearances for the Dutch national senior team while playing for Newcastle.

a. True

b. False

17. Gary Kelly joined which club after he left Newcastle?

a. Bury FC

b. Middlesbrough FC

c. Sheffield Wednesday

d. Fulham FC

18. How many appearances did Jimmy Lawrence make for the Scottish senior national team?

a. 1

b. 10

c. 17

d. 26

19. Martin Dúbravka was originally loaned to Newcastle by which side?

 a. Grasshopper Zürich

 b. FC Twente

 c. FC Zürich

 d. AC Sparta Prague

20. Rob Elliot conceded 40 goals in the 2015-16 domestic league.

 a. True

 b. False

QUIZ ANSWERS

1. C – Pavel Srníček

2. B – False

3. D – Jimmy Lawrence

4. D – Karl Darlow

5. C – 10

6. C – Steve Harper

7. B – False

8. D – 462

9. B – Martin Dúbravka

10. C – 8

11. A – Steve Harper

12. A – True

13. C – 496

14. D – Hull City FC

15. B – 89

16. B – False

17. A – Bury FC

18. A – 1

19. D – AC Sparta Prague

20. B – False

DID YOU KNOW?

1. One of the club's first goalkeepers was Matt Kingsley, who signed in 1898 from Darwen and made 180 league appearances and another nine in FA Cup contests. He joined West Ham United in 1904 after losing his starting spot to Jimmy Lawrence. He stayed with West Ham for just one season, during which he kicked former West Ham player Herbert Lyon during a match against Brighton & Hove Albion in March 1905, resulting in a pitch invasion and a near riot. In 1901, Kingsley became the first Newcastle player to earn a cap for England with a 6-0 win over Wales at St. James' Park.

2. Republic of Ireland international Shay Given played 462 times for Newcastle and appeared in 134 contests for his homeland to become the most-capped keeper for Ireland. Given is considered a club legend by fans because he helped the side qualify for Europe several times. He joined in 1997 from Blackburn and left for Manchester City in February 2009. Newcastle was relegated from the Premier League just a few months later. Given helped the side reach the 1997-98 FA Cup and win their group stage in the 2006 Intertoto Cup. He was also named Newcastle's Player of the Year for 2005-06 and a member of the PFA Premier League Team of the Year for 2001-02 and 2005-06.

3. Steve Harper is one of three goalkeepers who have been inducted into the Newcastle United Hall of Fame. He was the club's longest-serving player at 20 years from 1993 to 2013. Harper wasn't always the top-choice keeper, and when he played in the 1999 FA Cup final against Manchester United, it was just his 10th senior appearance. He took over the top spot in 2007-08 when Shay Given left, and once went 501 minutes without allowing a goal. He also holds the club record for clean sheets in a season, with 21, and he became the team's oldest player in Europe in 2012 when he was 37 years and 162 days of age. Harper became a Newcastle coach as well as a TV pundit after retiring.

4. Also in the club's Hall of Fame is former Czech Republic international Pavel Srníček, who arrived from his homeland in January 1991. He struggled early but established himself as the number-one in his second season when the club was promoted to the Premier League as First Division winners. He left St. James' Park in 1998, but Srníček returned at the age of 38 as an injury replacement in October 2006. Almost a decade had passed between appearances for the team, and he retired in 2007. Srníček sadly passed away on December 29, 2015, in his homeland at the age of 47 after suffering a heart attack.

5. The third keeper in the team's Hall of Fame is Jimmy Lawrence, who holds the club record for overall appearances at 496 and league appearances with 432. The native of Scotland joined from Hibernian in 1904 and

remained until retiring in 1922. During his 18 years with the team, he won three First Division titles and an FA Cup. He took over between the posts from an injured Charlie Watts and held the number-one job for nearly two decades. Lawrence is believed to be Newcastle's oldest-ever player by some historians due to an alleged mix-up with his birth certificate.

6. Dutch international Tim Krul kicked off his career with the Magpies from 2006 to 2017, appearing in nearly 200 games. He was loaned out in 2007-08 and 2008-09 and became a regular in 2010-11. He was then loaned to Ajax and AZ Alkmaar in his homeland for the 2016-17 campaign. Krul left the team in August 2017 when he joined Brighton & Hove Albion. He helped Newcastle win the second-tier Championship League in 2009-10, and, in the 2014 World Cup, he became the first goalie to come on as a substitute keeper for a penalty shootout. He promptly saved two of five kicks as Holland beat Costa Rica.

7. Willie McFaul was one of Newcastle's most consistent keepers. He played just under 300 games for the side. The Northern Ireland international joined from Linfield in 1966 and remained until hanging up his boots in 1975. He managed the club between 1985 and 1988 and went on to manage the Guam National Men's Team. McFaul helped the Magpies squad reach the 1973-74 FA Cup final against Liverpool, but the team suffered a 3-0 defeat.

8. After arriving in 1975 from Torquay United, Mike Mahoney appeared in over 100 matches with the Magpies.

He left in 1979 to continue his career in America and later managed an indoor soccer team in Los Angeles. He was part of the 1975-76 side that reached the League Cup final, which they lost 2-1 to Manchester City. Mahoney was still with the team when it was relegated from the First Division in 1977-78 and that's when his contract was sold to the Chicago Sting.

9. Ronnie Simpson was a Scottish international who played between the posts when Glasgow Celtic won the European Cup in Lisbon, Portugal, in 1966-67. However, before achieving that feat, he won the FA Cup with Newcastle in 1951-52 and 1954-55. He signed from Third Lanark in 1951 for a reported £8,750 and played nearly 300 games before joining Hibernian in 1960. Simpson also represented Great Britain at the 1948 Olympics. His father, Jimmy Simpson, was also a pro player and Scottish international. Ronnie passed away in 2004 and was inducted into the Scottish Football Hall of Fame in 2011.

10. After playing a couple of hundred times with Heart of Midlothian in Scotland and making his first-team debut as a 17-year-old, Gordon Marshall joined Newcastle in 1963 for a reported £18,000. He had already won five trophies in Scotland and then helped the Magpies capture the 1964-65 Second Division title. Marshall became the number-one with Newcastle until 1968 when he was sold to Nottingham Forest for a reported £17,500. His son, Gordon Jr., was a pro keeper and earned a cap for Scotland, while his son Scott was a defender for several

top-flight teams in England. Also, Marshall's daughter Lesley played with the National Scottish Basketball team.

CHAPTER 5:

DARING DEFENDERS

QUIZ TIME!

1. Which player appeared in more career games for Newcastle?

   a. David Craig
   b. Frank Hudspeth
   c. Alf McMichael
   d. Frank Clark

2. Federico Fernández was shown 10 yellow cards in the 2019-20 Premier League.

   a. True
   b. False

3. Which player scored two goals in the 1993-94 domestic league?

   a. Robbie Elliot
   b. Barry Venison
   c. Kevin Scott
   d. Steve Watson

4. Who made 40 appearances in all competitions in 2011-12?

   a. Danny Simpson
   b. Ryan Taylor
   c. Fabricio Coloccini
   d. Mike Williamson

5. How many goals did Fabian Schär score in the 2018-19 domestic league?

   a. 7
   b. 5
   c. 4
   d. 2

6. Barry Venison left which club to join Newcastle?

   a. Liverpool FC
   b. Sunderland AFC
   c. Sheffield United
   d. Southampton FC

7. Steven Taylor was named to the FIFPro XI squad in 2010-11.

   a. True
   b. False

8. Who made 35 appearances in all competitions in 2013-14?

   a. Mapou Yanga-Mbiwa
   b. Davide Santon
   c. Mathieu Debuchy
   d. Mike Williamson

9. How many appearances did Frank Clark make in all competitions?

   a. 487
   b. 457
   c. 431
   d. 375

10. How many goals did Colin Veitch score in all competitions for the Magpies?

    a. 22
    b. 38
    c. 49
    d. 55

11. Which player appeared in 45 matches in 2016-17?

    a. Jamaal Lascelles
    b. Paul Dummett
    c. DeAndre Yedlin
    d. Ciaran Clark

12. Fabricio Coloccini was named to the PWA Team of the Year in 2012.

    a. True
    b. False

13. Which player was shown two red cards in the 2003-04 Premier League?

    a. Andy Griffin
    b. Olivier Bernard
    c. Andrew O'Brien
    d. Titus Bramble

14. How many appearances did Frank Hudspeth make in all competitions?

    a. 382
    b. 450
    c. 472
    d. 496

15. Which young defender scored in his home debut on January 1, 2007?

    a. José Enrique
    b. David Edgar
    c. Stephen Carr
    d. Steven Taylor

16. José Enrique was shown three red cards in all competitions in 2009-10.

    a. True
    b. False

17. How many assists did Ryan Taylor tally in all competitions in 2009-10?

    a. 10
    b. 7
    c. 6
    d. 3

18. How many appearances did Alf McMichael make in all competitions?

    a. 366
    b. 385

c. 431

d. 470

19. Which player appeared in 38 matches in all competitions in 2000-01?

   a. Aaron Hughes

   b. Warren Barton

   c. Andy Griffin

   d. Alain Goma

20. Frank Hudspeth played 15 games for the English national team.

   a. True

   b. False

QUIZ ANSWERS

1. B – Frank Hudspeth

2. B – False

3. D – Steve Watson

4. A – Danny Simpson

5. C – 4

6. A – Liverpool FC

7. B – False

8. D – Mike Williamson

9. B – 457

10. C – 49

11. B – Paul Dummett

12. A – True

13. C – Andrew O'Brien

14. C – 472

15. B – David Edgar

16. B – False

17. C – 6

18. C – 431

19. A – Aaron Hughes

20. B – False

DID YOU KNOW?

1. Newcastle United Hall-of-Famer Frank Clark played 457 games with the club between 1962 and 1975 to rank fourth all-time in Newcastle appearances. He joined from Crook Town in October 1962 and eventually left for Nottingham Forest. He became a regular in 1964-65 when the side lifted the Second Division championship. In 1968-69, he helped the team capture the European (Inter-Cities) Fairs Cup and reach the 1973-74 FA Cup final. Clark later won the league title and European Cup with Nottingham Forest and also managed the club.

2. Another Hall of Fame defender named Frank was Scottish international Frank Brennan. He joined the side just after World War II from Airdrieonians in 1946 for a reported £7,500 and played one game shy of 350 over the next decade before retiring. The defensive colossus helped the side win back-to-back FA Cups in 1951 and 1952 but was controversially dropped from the team that won the 1955 FA Cup. Brennan was known as the "Rock of Tyneside" and also helped the team earn promotion back to Division 1 in 1947-48. He later became a football manager.

3. Let's be frank one more time with legendary 5-foot-7-inch defender Frank Hudspeth, who spent 19 years with Newcastle from 1910 to 1929. Nicknamed "Old Surefoot " due to his dependability, he wore the captain's armband

between 1923 and 1926 and was an expert penalty-taker with 25 of his 37 goals coming from the spot. Hudspeth played 472 times with the team to rank second in all-time appearances behind goalkeeper Jimmy Lawrence. However, he played for England just once. He helped Newcastle win the 1923-24 FA Cup and the 1926-27 First Division.

4. David Edgar was a Canadian international who grew up playing ice hockey and participating in track and field before concentrating on soccer. He joined the Newcastle academy as a 14-year-old when leaving Canada to live with his grandmother. He debuted for the first team in December 2006 and scored in his home debut on New Year's Day 2007, against Manchester United. He was named man of the match in the 2-2 draw after marking Cristiano Ronaldo as well as scoring. In 2008-09, the team was relegated from the Premier League, and Edgar joined Burnley. His father, Eddie Edgar, was a pro goalkeeper who played briefly for the Magpies.

5. During his tenure with the club, David Craig of Northern Ireland made 435 appearances. He began his residency at St. James' Park as a youth player and helped his side win the 1961-62 FA Youth Cup by edging Wolverhampton Wanderers 2-1. After breaking into the senior squad, Craig played another 14 years. He was part of the teams that hoisted the 1968-69 European (Inter-Cities) Fairs Cup and the minor Texaco Cup and Anglo-Italian Cup. Unfortunately, he missed both the 1973-74 FA Cup final

and the 1975-76 League Cup final due to injury. Craig hung up his boots in 1978 and was inducted into the Newcastle United Hall of Fame in 2019.

6. Belgian international Philippe Albert joined Newcastle from Anderlecht for a reported £2.6 million in 1994. He turned down moves to Juventus and Fiorentina in Italy because he didn't want to play on Sundays and didn't like the hot weather. He became a cult hero with Magpies fans for his attacking forays, and the team itself was known as "The Entertainers" in this period. Albert had injury problems and was loaned in 1998-99 to third-tier club Fulham, helping the team win the Second Division title. He left for Charleroi in Belgium in 1999 for a reported £600,000 after just over 130 games with the Magpies.

7. The first decade of Bob Stokoe's career was spent with the Magpies from 1950 to 1960 with the side winning FA Cups in 1950-51, 1951-52, and 1954-55. He signed in 1947 as an apprentice and appeared in over 260 games with the squad while scoring on his debut. Stokoe later became a player-manager with Bury. After hanging up his boots in 1965, he went on to manage several other clubs with two stints each at Bury, Rochdale, Blackpool, Carlisle United, and Sunderland, where he won an FA Cup and Second Division title. There's a statue of Stokoe outside of Sunderland's Stadium of Light.

8. Left-back Alf McMichael was a Northern Ireland international who played 431 games for Newcastle between 1949 and 1962 to rank sixth on the all-time

appearance list. He joined from Linfield and helped the team win FA Cups in 1950-51, 1951-52, and 1954-55. However, he missed the 1951 final due to injury. McMichael was one of the league's best defenders, but the scoring touch certainly evaded him as he managed to notch just one goal for the side. He also went without a goal in 40 matches with his homeland before turning to football management.

9. Wilf Low, known as the "Laughing Cavalier," was one of the Magpies' toughest defenders between 1909 and 1924. The Scottish international arrived from Aberdeen and played 367 times for Newcastle, chipping in with eight goals. He helped the club win the FA Cup in 1909-10 and 1923-24. After hanging up his boots, Low remained with the team as a coach and then as the club's groundsman. His brother Harry and son Norman were also professional soccer players. Low passed away at the age of 48 in 1933 when he was struck by an automobile.

10. Republic of Ireland international John Anderson spent a decade at St. James' Park after signing from Preston North End in 1982 on a free transfer. He played just under 340 games before retiring and contributed 14 goals. In 1983-84, he helped the team earn promotion back to the First Division playing alongside teammates Chris Waddle, Kevin Keegan, Peter Beardsley, and Terry McDermott. Anderson played 41 of 42 league games that campaign. He went on to work as an analyst for soccer matches with RTÉ radio and BBC Radio Newcastle.

CHAPTER 6:
MAESTROS OF THE MIDFIELD

QUIZ TIME!

1. Which player made more appearances for Newcastle?

   a. Gary Speed

   b. Lee Clark

   c. Kieron Dyer

   d. David McCreery

2. Stephen Glass tallied eight assists in the 1998-99 Premier League.

   a. True

   b. False

3. Which player notched five goals in all competitions in 2010-11?

   a. James Perch

   b. Alan Smith

   c. Joey Barton

   d. Shane Ferguson

4. How many league goals did Chris Waddle score with Newcastle?

    a. 36
    b. 48
    c. 46
    d. 64

5. Which club did James Milner leave to join Newcastle?

    a. Aston Villa
    b. Southampton FC
    c. West Ham United
    d. Leeds United

6. Which player made 44 appearances in the 2009-10 domestic league?

    a. Alan Smith
    b. Jonás Gutiérrez
    c. Danny Guthrie
    d. Kevin Nolan

7. Gary Speed won the FWA Footballer of the Year award in 2002-03.

    a. True
    b. False

8. What was Paul Gascoigne's nickname?

    a. The Dazzler
    b. Diesel
    c. Gazza
    d. Two-foot Terror

9. Which player was sold to Tottenham Hotspur in July 1997?

   a. Nicky Butt
   b. David Batty
   c. David Ginola
   d. Paul Gascoigne

10. Which player made 47 appearances in all competitions in 2016-17?

   a. Jonjo Shelvey
   b. Isaac Hayden
   c. Jack Colback
   d. Mohamed Diamé

11. Which player scored seven goals in the 1993-94 Premier League?

   a. Scott Sellars
   b. Rob Lee
   c. Paul Bracewell
   d. Chris Holland

12. Lee Bowyer was shown 11 yellow cards in all competitions in 2003-04.

   a. True
   b. False

13. From which club did Gary Speed join Newcastle?

   a. Swansea City
   b. Manchester United
   c. Peterborough United
   d. Everton

14. Which player had seven assists in the 2014-15 domestic league?

    a. Siem de Jong

    b. Jonás Gutiérrez

    c. Jack Colback

    d. Moussa Sissako

15. Which player scored six goals in the 1998-99 Premier League?

    a. Nolberto Solano

    b. Gary Speed

    c. Stephen Glass

    d. Dietmar Hamann

16. Four different midfielders were shown a red card in the 2004-05 Premier League.

    a. True

    b. False

17. How many stints did Terry McDermott have with the Magpies?

    a. 0

    b. 1

    c. 2

    d. 3

18. Georginio Wijnaldum played for which club before coming to Newcastle?

    a. Ajax

    b. FC Twente

c. PSV Eindhoven

d. Sparta Rotterdam

19. Who scored eight goals in all competitions in 2006-07?

a. Scott Parker

b. James Milner

c. Kieron Dyer

d. Antoine Sibierski

20. Mohamed Diamé scored 10 goals in the 2017-18 Premier League.

a. True

b. False

QUIZ ANSWERS

1. A – Gary Speed

2. B – False

3. C – Joey Barton

4. C – 46

5. D – Leeds United

6. D – Kevin Nolan

7. B – False

8. C – Gazza

9. C – David Ginola

10. A – Jonjo Shelvey

11. B – Rob Lee

12. A – True

13. D – Everton

14. C – Jack Colback

15. A – Nolberto Solano

16. B – False

17. C – 2

18. C – PSV Eindhoven

19. D – Antoine Sibierski

20. B – False

DID YOU KNOW?

1. Terry McDermott enjoyed two stints at St. James' Park as both a player and assistant manager. He played from 1973 to 1974 after arriving from Bury and before leaving for Liverpool and returned eight years later to play from 1982 to 1984. He helped the side reach the 1973-74 FA Cup final against Liverpool and later helped it earn promotion to the First Division in 1983-84. The English international played just under 120 games with the Magpies and chipped in with 17 goals before joining Cork City in January 1985.

2. Chris Waddle began his pro journey with Newcastle, from 1980, when he was 19 years old, to 1985. The English international was known for his dribbling skills and earned the nickname "Magic Chris." He helped the side earn promotion to the top flight in 1983-84 and was named to the First Division PFA Team of the Year for 1984-85. He tallied 46 goals in 170 league outings before joining Tottenham Hotspur in July 1985 for £590,000. In 1987, Waddle and Spurs teammate Glenn Hoddle recorded a song named "Diamond Lights" which reached number 12 in the UK Singles Chart, and the duo later appeared on the famous *Top of the Pops* TV show.

3. French international David Ginola joined in 1995 for a reported £2.5 million and helped the team finish second in

the Premier League. It was seen as a disappointment by the squad and manager Kevin Keegan, though, as they had led eventual winners Manchester United by 10 points in January. The Magpies finished second to Man United again the following season, with Keegan being replaced by Kenny Dalglish midway through the campaign. Ginola and Kenny Dalglish didn't see eye to eye, and he was sold to Tottenham in July 1997 for a reported £2.5 million. Ginola later dabbled in acting and winemaking and became a television pundit.

4. One of the greatest players and characters in soccer history, English international Paul Gascoigne began his pro career with Newcastle, from 1985 to 1988. "Gazza" dazzled fans and opponents in just over 100 games while netting 25 goals. He captained Newcastle's youth side to the FA Youth Cup in 1984-85, scoring twice in the final. One of his most infamous incidents with the Magpies came in 1988 when Vinnie Jones of Wimbledon was photographed grabbing Gascoigne by the genitals during a game. In 1987-88, Gazza was named the PFA Young Player of the Year and made the PFA Premier League Team of the Year. He then signed with Tottenham Hotspur for a then British-record £2.2 million.

5. Nolberto Solano was the first Peruvian to play in an FA Cup final and in the Premier League. Known as "Nobby," he arrived from Boca Juniors in Argentina in 1998 and helped the side reach the 1999 FA Cup final. He joined Aston Villa in January 2004 but returned in August 2005

while young midfielder James Milner joined Villa on a season-long loan as part of the transaction. Solano then joined West Ham United in 2007 after playing over 300 games with the Magpies. Solano was an accomplished trumpet player and formed a salsa band known as The Geordie Latinos. He was quite popular in Peru, played 95 times for the national team, and had his wedding televised live on television there.

6. Kieron Dyer was sold to Newcastle from Ipswich Town in 1999 for a reported £6 million fee, which, at the time, made him the most expensive Ipswich player ever sold. He made 250 appearances for the Magpies until 2007 when he was sold to West Ham United for the same fee. The English international played 33 times for his homeland and became an Ipswich coach after hanging up his boots. He appeared on the British reality television show *I'm a Celebrity...Get Me Out of Here!* and donated his fee to charity. Dyer was named to the PFA Premier Team of the Year for 2002-03 with the Magpies.

7. After joining from Bolton Wanderers in January 2009 for a reported £4 million, Kevin Nolan played just under 100 games for the club before joining West Ham United two years later. The team was relegated to the second-tier Championship League at the end of the season, and Nolan was appointed captain for a stint the next campaign. He was named the Championship Player of the Year for 2009-10 when he helped the side earn promotion back to the Premier League by winning the

Championship League. Nolan was named club captain for 2010-11 but left for West Ham after the season where he became the team's skipper.

8. Northern Ireland international Tommy Cassidy signed from Glentoran for a reported £15,000 in 1970, and he stayed for a decade. However, he didn't become a regular starter until three seasons into his stint. The attacking midfielder helped the team win the 1973 and 1974 Anglo-Italian Cups and the 1974 Texaco Cup. He also appeared in an FA Cup and a League Cup final, taking home runner-up medals each time. Cassidy played 24 times for Northern Ireland and over 150 games with the Magpies before joining Burnley for £30,000 in 1980.

9. Liam O'Brien was a Republic of Ireland international who arrived at St. James' Park from Manchester United in November 1988 for a reported £275,000. The team was relegated after his first season, but O'Brien was a key member of the squad that won the second-tier First Division title in 1992-93 to reach the Premier League for the first time. However, once there, O'Brien found playing time harder to come by, and he was sold to Tranmere Rovers for a reported £350,000 after playing just over 150 games for the Magpies.

10. After kicking off his pro career in his native Georgia in 1987 with Dinamo Tbilisi, Temuri "Temur" Ketsbaia found himself playing for AEK Athens in Greece a few years later. He then joined Newcastle in 1997 on a free

transfer. He scored in extra time against Croatia Zagreb, sending the Magpies to the European Cup/Champions League for the very first time. Ketsbaia became another cult hero with Newcastle supporters, but he was sold to Wolverhampton Wanderers in 2000. He retired in 2007 and entered the world of football management, including a stint with the Georgian national team with whom he had played 52 times.

CHAPTER 7:

SENSATIONAL STRIKERS & FORWARDS

QUIZ TIME!

1. Which player made more appearances in all competitions for Newcastle?

   a. Jackie Milburn

   b. Alan Shearer

   c. Bobby Mitchell

   d. Shola Ameobi

2. Dwight Gayle posted 12 assists in all competitions in 2016-17.

   a. True

   b. False

3. Which player scored 21 goals in the 1993-94 Premier League?

   a. Malcolm Allen

   b. Peter Beardsley

   c. Lee Clark

   d. Alex Mathie

4. Andy Cole was playing for which club before joining Newcastle?

   a. Sunderland AFC
   b. Birmingham City FC
   c. Arsenal FC
   d. Bristol City FC

5. How many appearances did Bobby Mitchell make in all competitions for the Magpies?

   a. 433
   b. 410
   c. 385
   d. 366

6. How many goals did Salomón Rondón score in the 2018-19 domestic league?

   a. 4
   b. 8
   c. 11
   d. 15

7. Alan Shearer scored a total of 30 goals for the senior English national team.

   a. True
   b. False

8. How many goals did Shola Ameobi score in all competitions for Newcastle?

   a. 52
   b. 63

c. 79

d. 88

9. Who was nicknamed "The Newcastle Flyer"?

   a. Ivor Allchurch

   b. Faustino Asprilla

   c. John "Jock" Rutherford

   d. Alan Shearer

10. Who won the 1996 PFA Players' Player of the Year award?

    a. Les Ferdinand

    b. Paul Brayson

    c. Paul Kitson

    d. Faustino Asprilla

11. How many appearances did Jackie Milburn make in all competitions?

    a. 415

    b. 397

    c. 366

    d. 340

12. Andy Cole scored 58 goals in 55 games in all competitions for Newcastle.

    a. True

    b. False

13. Which player appeared in 36 matches in the 2017-18 domestic league?

a. Christian Atsu

b. Kenedy

c. Dwight Gayle

d. Ayoze Pérez

14. Who recorded 19 goals in all competitions in 2009-10?

a. Fabrice Pancrate

b. Wayne Routledge

c. Peter Lövenkrands

d. Andy Carroll

15. How many goals did Demba Ba score in his 58 matches in all competitions with Newcastle?

a. 35

b. 29

c. 13

d. 9

16. Alan Shearer finished third in voting for the FIFA World Player of the Year award in 1997.

a. True

b. False

17. Who won the PFA Young Player of the Year award in 2002?

a. Craig Bellamy

b. Laurent Robert

c. Shola Ameobi

d. Carl Cort

18. What was Malcolm Macdonald's nickname?

a. Supermac

b. Hammerhead

c. Mac Attack

d. Steel Foot

19. Which player tallied nine goals in the 2015-16 domestic league?

a. Andros Townsend

b. Papiss Demba Cissé

c. Ayoze Pérez

d. Aleksander Mitrović

20. Laurent Robert registered 20 assists in all competitions in 2001-02.

a. True

b. False

QUIZ ANSWERS

1. C – Bobby Mitchell

2. B – False

3. B – Peter Beardsley

4. D – Bristol City FC

5. B – 410

6. C – 11

7. A – True

8. C – 79

9. C – John "Jock" Rutherford

10. A – Les Ferdinand

11. B – 397

12. B – False

13. D – Ayoze Pérez

14. D – Andy Carroll

15. B – 29

16. B – False

17. A – Craig Bellamy

18. A – Supermac

19. D – Aleksander Mitrović

20. B – False

DID YOU KNOW?

1. Duncan Ferguson arrived from Everton in 1998 and returned there two years later. In between, he played just over 40 games with Newcastle, scoring twice in his debut. He was one of the most colorful characters to play at St. James' Park and had one of the greatest nicknames in sports history, "Duncan Disorderly," a superb play on words due to his four convictions for assault. He was a highly entertaining, mischievous player who shares the Premier League record with eight red cards. Ferguson was fearless and unpredictable and once paid for headbutting an opponent with a three-month jail sentence. Ferguson's home was broken into twice with perpetrators spending time in hospital on both occasions after he got hold of them.

2. Although he was born in Nigeria, striker Shola Ameobi grew up near St. James' Park and spent his youth career with the club. He went on to notch 79 goals in 397 outings and quickly became a Newcastle cult hero due to his performances and loyalty to the club. Ameobi helped the side win its 2006 Intertoto Cup group stage and the second-tier Championship League in 2009-10. He played with the first team from 2000 to 2014 before heading to Turkey. Ameobi was inducted into the Newcastle United Hall of Fame in 2017 and returned to the club in 2019 as a loan manager.

3. One of the most underrated players in English soccer history was international forward Les Ferdinand, the cousin of fellow players Rio, Anton, and Kane Ferdinand. He arrived from Queens Park Rangers in 1995 for a reported £6 million and joined Tottenham Hotspur two years later for the same price. Known as "Sir Les," he notched 29 goals in his first season and won Premier League runner-up medals in both of his Magpies campaigns. He posted 50 goals in 84 games, was named the PFA Players' Player of the Year in 1995-96, and also made the Premier League PFA Team of the Year. Ferdinand was inducted into the Newcastle United Hall of Fame in 2017.

4. Kevin Keegan's name will forever be linked with Newcastle as a player and manager. Known as "King Kev" on Tyneside, he was one of his generation's greatest players. He arrived from Southampton in 1982, a few seasons after being named European Player of the Year twice with Hamburg. At just 5 feet 8 inches tall, he scored 21 times in 63 games for England and notched 48 goals in 78 league games with the Magpies while helping them earn promotion from the Second Division in 1983-84. He left Newcastle at the end of the season and famously departed the pitch in a helicopter following his final game. Keegan was also inducted into the club's Hall of Fame.

5. Nicknamed "The Newcastle Flyer," John "Jock" Rutherford became the club's youngest player and scorer

at the age of 17 in 1902. He netted 94 goals in 336 games and played 11 games with England. He joined Arsenal in 1913, played 23 years in total before hanging up his boots when in his 40s, and became that club's oldest player. Rutherford helped the Magpies win three First Division titles while playing in five FA Cup finals, winning one of them. The club Hall-of-Famer's great-grandson, Greg, won a gold medal in the long jump at the 2012 Olympics in London, and his brothers Bob and Sep were pro soccer players.

6. Colombian international Faustino Asprilla carved a name for himself with Parma before signing with Newcastle in February 1996 for a reported £6.7 million. Known as "Tino," he won a pair of runner-up medals in the Premier League in his first two seasons. He notched five goals in the team's UEFA Cup campaign but celebrated too hard after scoring against Metz and was ejected with a second yellow card and suspended for the next match. Asprilla scored all the team's goals in a 3-2 European Champions League win over Barcelona in 1997-98 before being sold back to Parma for a reported £6 million. He scored just nine goals in 48 league matches but tallied nine in only 11 European games.

7. Ivor Allchurch, known as the "Golden Boy of Welsh football," joined Newcastle in 1958 at the age of 28 from Swansea Town, where he's still the club's all-time leading scorer. He scored twice in his Magpies debut and went on to net 51 goals in 154 appearances. The team was

relegated to the Second Division following the 1960-61 campaign, and Allchurch played one more season before joining Cardiff City. He was inducted into the Welsh Sports Hall of Fame and the English Football Hall of Fame, and there is a statue in his honor outside of the Liberty Stadium in Swansea.

8. Albert Shepherd suited up for the Magpies between 1908 and 1914 after joining from Bolton Wanderers and before leaving for Bradford City. He helped the side win the First Division title in 1908-09 and became the first squad player to score 30 goals in a season when he hit 31. This was achieved in 1909-10 when he also helped the team win the FA Cup by scoring both goals in a 2-0 win over Barnsley in the final. He notched 31 again the next season to lead the league. Shepherd played just twice for England and scored two goals for his homeland. He missed a year of action due to a knee injury, was sold to Bradford City, and retired a year later. He scored nearly 100 goals for the Magpies in 123 games.

9. Chilean international Jorge Oliver signed with the club in January 1949 for £26,500 from Barnsley, and the transfer fee included his brother Ted because Jorge wouldn't sign without him. In 1950-51, he became the first South American to play in the FA Cup final with Newcastle, which downed Blackpool 2-0. He led the First Division in scoring in 1951-52, with 33 goals, and he tallied 39 in all competitions. Jorge then scored in the FA Cup final against Arsenal to win a second straight trophy. That goal

was made famous by ex-Beatle John Lennon, who included it on the cover of his *Walls and Bridges* album in 1974. He scored 91 times in 166 matches before joining Colo-Colo in Chile.

10. Michael "Micky" Quinn signed from Portsmouth in July 1989 for a reported £680,000 and proceeded to bang in four goals in his debut and lead the Second Division in scoring with 34 goals while netting 39 in all competitions. He followed up with 20 goals for the team the next season but managed just seven in 22 matches in 1991-92 due to a knee injury. He was sold to Coventry City in November 1992 for a reported £250,000 after scoring 77 times in 110 outings for the Magpies.

CHAPTER 8:

NOTABLE TRANSFERS & SIGNINGS

QUIZ TIME!

1. Who is the club's most expensive signing as of 2021?

    a. Michael Owen
    b. Joelinton
    c. Miguel Almirón
    d. Callum Wilson

2. Newcastle signed Alan Shearer for a then record-breaking transfer fee of £10 million.

    a. True
    b. False

3. Who was the most expensive player Newcastle has sold as of 2021?

    a. Ayoze Pérez
    b. Georginio Wijnaldum
    c. Andy Carroll
    d. Moussa Sissako

4. Who was the club's most expensive signing in 2008-09?

   a. Xisco
   b. Fabricio Coloccini
   c. Alan Smith
   d. Jonás Gutiérrez

5. Newcastle sold Andy Carroll to which side in 2010-11?

   a. Chelsea FC
   b. Tottenham Hotspur
   c. West Ham United
   d. Liverpool FC

6. How much did Newcastle receive for selling Ayoze Pérez?

   a. £16 million
   b. £22.5 million
   c. £27 million
   d. £30.06 million

7. Newcastle signed eight players for at least £10 million each in 2015-16.

   a. True
   b. False

8. Which player did the club transfer to Aston Villa for a fee of £13 million in 2008-09?

   a. James Milner
   b. Shay Given
   c. Scott Parker
   d. Obafemi Martins

9. What was the transfer fee Newcastle paid to sign Joelinton?

   a. £47 million
   b. £32.5 million
   c. £45 million
   d. £39.6 million

10. Which player was the club's most expensive signing in 1999-2000?

   a. Kieron Dyer
   b. Alain Goma
   c. Duncan Ferguson
   d. Dietmar Hamann

11. How much did the club receive when it sold Andy Carroll?

   a. £40 million
   b. £36.9 million
   c. £28.5 million
   d. £23 million

12. Newcastle signed Andy Cole for a reported fee of £3 million.

   a. True
   b. False

13. From which club did Newcastle acquire Joelinton?

   a. Valencia CF
   b. SC Recife
   c. TSG Hoffenheim
   d. Rapid Vienna

14. How much was the transfer fee Newcastle paid to acquire Matt Ritchie from Bournemouth FC?

    a. £3 million
    b. £5 million
    c. £7 million
    d. £10 million

15. Who was the club's most expensive signing in 2003-04?

    a. Craig Bellamy
    b. Laurent Robert
    c. Hugo Viana
    d. Jonathan Woodgate

16. Newcastle paid over £6 million for Matz Sels, who only made 14 appearances in all competitions.

    a. True
    b. False

17. How much did Newcastle pay to sign Michael Owen?

    a. £36 million
    b. £30 million
    c. £22.5 million
    d. £18 million

18. Newcastle sold which player to Fulham FC in 2018-19?

    a. Florian Thauvin
    b. Chancel Mbemba
    c. Aleksander Mitrović
    d. Mikel Merino

19. From which club did Newcastle sign Papiss Demba Cissé from in 2011-12?

    a. FC Schalke 04
    b. FC Metz
    c. AS Douanes
    d. SC Freiburg

20. Newcastle signed three players for £5 million each in 2013-14.

    a. True
    b. False

QUIZ ANSWERS

1. B – Joelinton

2. B – False

3. C – Andy Carroll

4. B – Fabricio Coloccini

5. D – Liverpool FC

6. D – £30.06 million

7. B – False

8. A – James Milner

9. D – £39.6 million

10. A – Kieron Dyer

11. B – £36.9 million

12. B – False

13. C – TSG Hoffenheim

14. D – £10 million

15. D – Jonathan Woodgate

16. A – True

17. C – £22.5 million

18. C – Aleksander Mitrović

19. D – SC Freiburg

20. B – False

DID YOU KNOW?

1. The top five transfer fees paid by Newcastle as of March 2021 are: forward Joelinton (Joelinton Cássio Apolinário de Lira) from TSG 1899 for £39.6 million in 2019-20, forward Michael Owen from Real Madrid for £22.5 million in 2005-06, midfielder Miguel Almirón from Atlanta United FC for £21.6 million in 2018-19, forward Callum Wilson from AFC Bournemouth for £20.03 million in 2020-21, and forward Alan Shearer from Blackburn Rovers for £18.9 million in 1996-97.

2. The top five transfer fees received by the club as of March 2021 are: forward Andy Carroll to Liverpool FC for £36.9 million in 2010-11, midfielder Moussa Sissako to Tottenham Hotspur for £31.5 million in 2016-17, forward Ayoze Pérez to Leicester City for £30.06 million in 2019-20, midfielder Georginio Wijnaldum to Liverpool FC for £24.75 million in 2016-17, and midfielder Yohan Cabaye to Paris Saint-Germain for £22.5 million in 2013-14.

3. When Andy Carroll was sold to Liverpool in January 2011, the move was made after Liverpool sold Spanish international striker Fernando Torres to Chelsea for £50 million. Manager Kenny Dalglish apparently panicked because Liverpool had no experienced striker, and he bought English international Carroll for £36.9 million. This set a new record for a British player, but Carroll

scored just 11 goals in 58 games at Liverpool after notching 33 in 91 matches with the Magpies. Liverpool eventually sold Carroll to West Ham United for £15.75 million. He rejoined the Magpies in August 2019 on a free transfer after scoring 32 goals in 142 outings for West Ham. As of March 2021, he was still with the club.

4. Striker Andy Cole holds Newcastle's record for goals in a season in all competitions with 41 in 1993-94. He was bought in February 1993 from Bristol City for a reported £1.75 million. The English international scored 12 goals in his first 12 appearances as the side won the First Division. He scored 34 league goals the next season to set a Premier League record in a 42-game campaign and became the fastest to score 50 times in the division by doing so in 65 games. Cole was also named the PFA Young Player of the Year for the season. With 68 goals in 84 games, it came as a shock when Cole was sold to Manchester United in January 1995 for a British record fee of a reported £6 million while Keith Gillespie joined the Magpies from Man United as part of the transaction.

5. After Northern Ireland international winger Keith Gillespie arrived at St. James' Park from Manchester United in the Andy Cole transaction in January 1995, he went on to play just under 150 games and chipped in with 14 goals. He played in the European Champions League and UEFA Cup with the squad and helped it finish as Premier League runner-up in 1995-96 and 1996-97, with Man United winning the title both seasons. Gillespie also

helped the team reach the 1997-98 FA Cup final but missed the defeat to Arsenal due to injury. He was then sold for a reported £2.3 million to Blackburn Rovers in 1998.

6. Goalkeeper Matz Sels was secured from KAA Gent in his Belgian homeland in June 2016 for a reported £6.5 million as manager Rafael Benítez's first signing for the club. Sels became the most expensive keeper in club annals but played just nine league games and 14 in total that season with the Magpies, who won their second-tier Championship League title. He was loaned to Anderlecht just 12 months after arriving, then left Newcastle for good in June 2018 when he was sold to Strasbourg for a reported £3.5 million.

7. Young Brazilian striker Joelinton Cássio Apolinário de Lira, who's simply known as Joelinton, joined Newcastle in July 2019 for a club-record transfer fee of £39.6 million and reportedly signed a six-year deal. He scored his first Premier League goal on August 25 but didn't tally again until January 14, 2020, when he scored in an FA Cup outing. Joelinton played four times for the Brazilian Under-17 national side in 2012 and scored twice, but, as of March 2021, the 24-year-old had just seven goals in his first 69 games with the Magpies and only three in 58 league outings.

8. Paraguayan international midfielder Miguel Almirón joined MLS club Atlanta United in America in 2017. The

attacker starred with the team and was named to the league's Best XI in 2017 and won the Newcomer of the Year award. He made the MLS Best XI again in 2018 and helped Atlanta win the MLS Cup in its second season of existence. Almirón joined Newcastle in January 2019 for £21.6 million to set a Newcastle and MLS record at the time. He played just 10 games his first season due to injury but led the team in goals in 2019-20 with eight. Almirón was still with the Magpies in March 2021 and had posted 13 goals in his first 78 career outings.

9. English international striker Callum Wilson was bought from Bournemouth for £20.03 million in September 2020 to become the club's third-highest purchase. He scored 67 goals in 187 games with Bournemouth and helped them win a second-tier title and was named to the PFA League One Team of the Year for 2013-14. He scored in his Magpies debut then netted his 50th career Premier League marker on January 30, 2021. Wilson started his Newcastle career in fine form, and by March 2021, he had chipped in with 10 goals in his first 19 league games.

10. French international midfielder Moussa Sissako was bought from French side Toulouse in January 2013 for £1.8 million and sold to Tottenham Hotspur in August 2016 for £31.5 million for a healthy profit. With Newcastle, he played just over 130 games and registered 12 goals, two of them in his second match. He wore the captain's armband for a spell in 2014-15 when Fabricio Coloccini was injured and wore it again for a brief time at the end of

2015-16. However, the team was relegated from the Premier League at the end of the campaign, and Sissako was sold a few months later.

CHAPTER 9:

ODDS & ENDS

QUIZ TIME!

1. Newcastle's biggest league victory was a 13-0 win against which club?

   a. Fulham FC

   b. Newport County

   c. Manchester City

   d. Nottingham City

2. St. James' Park is the 10th largest soccer stadium in England.

   a. True

   b. False

3. How many games did the club win in its first season in the Football League Second Division?

   a. 7

   b. 12

   c. 15

   d. 20

4. The Tyne-Wear Derby is a rivalry between Newcastle and which club?

   a. Sunderland AFC
   b. Hull City FC
   c. Leeds United
   d. Liverpool FC

5. Who is the oldest player to make an appearance for the club, at 44 years and 225 days?

   a. Stuart Pearce
   b. Steve Harper
   c. Pavel Srníček
   d. Billy Hampson

6. Which club makes up the other half of the Tyne-Tees derby?

   a. Leeds United
   b. Middlesbrough FC
   c. Fulham FC
   d. Sunderland AFC

7. The fastest recorded goal scored by a Newcastle player was 11 seconds.

   a. True
   b. False

8. How many matches did the squad draw in the 2003-04 domestic league?

   a. 17
   b. 12

c. 10

d. 6

9. What is the most games Newcastle has won in a Premier League season?

   a. 30

   b. 28

   c. 27

   d. 24

10. Which player scored the team's fastest recorded goal?

   a. Jackie Milburn

   b. Alan Shearer

   c. Malcolm Macdonald

   d. Pop Robson

11. Newcastle and Portsmouth played in a historic match that featured what?

   a. It was the first match to implement the substitution rule.

   b. The game had a brawl that resulted in a combined seven players being ejected.

   c. It was the first English league match played under floodlights.

   d. It was the first recorded game played in snow.

12. The most goals the side has scored in any domestic league season is 98 as of 2020.

   a. True

   b. False

13. What is the most games Newcastle has won in a Championship League season as of 2020?

    a. 21
    b. 25
    c. 28
    d. 30

14. Newcastle's biggest league defeat was 9-0 to what club?

    a. Manchester United
    b. West Ham United
    c. Burton Wanderers
    d. Aston Villa

15. Who is the youngest player to make an appearance for the club, at the age of 16 years and 233 days?

    a. Steve Watson
    b. Harris Vučkić
    c. Adam Armstrong
    d. Andy Carroll

16. Newcastle shared the record for best top-flight finish by a promoted club when they finished 3rd in the 1993-94 Premier League.

    a. True
    b. False

17. How many games did the side lose in the 1977-78 league campaign?

    a. 19
    b. 23

c. 26

d. 29

18. Who was the first Magpies player named to the PFA Premier League Team of the Year?

    a. Peter Beardsley

    b. Les Ferdinand

    c. Rob Lee

    d. David Ginola

19. Which player has NOT been inducted into the European Football Hall of Fame?

    a. Len Shackleton

    b. Peter Beardsley

    c. Alan Shearer

    d. Kevin Keegan

20. In a 2010 match against Wolverhampton Wanderers, both clubs were shown a combined 12 yellow cards.

    a. True

    b. False

QUIZ ANSWERS

1. B – Newport County

2. B – False

3. C – 15

4. A – Sunderland AFC

5. D – Billy Hampson

6. B – Middlesbrough FC

7. A – True

8. A – 17

9. D – 24

10. B – Alan Shearer

11. C – It was the first English league match played under floodlights.

12. A – True

13. D – 30

14. C – Burton Wanderers

15. A – Steve Watson

16. A – True

17. C – 26

18. A – Peter Beardsley

19. A – Len Shackleton

20. A – True

DID YOU KNOW?

1. Newcastle has its own Hall of Fame. Current members are Shola Ameobi, Peter Beardsley, Frank Brennan, Frank Clark, Les Ferdinand, Hughie Gallacher, Steve Harper, Joe Harvey, Kevin Keegan, Jimmy Lawrence, Malcolm Macdonald, Bill McCracken, Bobby Mitchell, Jackie Milburn, Bob Moncur, Jock Rutherford, Alan Shearer, Pavel Srníček, Colin Veitch, and manager Sir Bobby Robson.

2. The team first placed a crest on its shirts in 1911. It featured the city's coat of arms, but it wasn't adopted as an official emblem until 1969. The Newcastle upon Tyne coat of arms depicts the city's history by featuring a Norman-era castle and two seahorses. The crest section shows a demi-lion sitting atop the city's historic castle keep that flies the swallow-tailed pennon of the Arms of Saint George. The coat of arms also includes the city's Latin motto, *Fortiter Defendit Triumphans*, which means "triumphing by brave defense."

3. The first club-specific crest was designed in 1976, and new crests were designed in 1983 and 1988. There was also a 125th anniversary crest for the 2017-18 season. The crest was featured on the team's classic black-and-white-striped home shirts and on the away kit during the historic season.

4. Newcastle United FC has been owned by Newcastle United Limited since 2007. The company is a subsidiary of MASH Holdings Limited, which is owned by Mike Ashley. The team plays its home games at St. James' Park in Newcastle, which has a capacity of 52,338. The venue is currently the eighth-largest for soccer in England.

5. The first organized game hosted at St. James' Park took place in 1880, 12 years before Newcastle United was formed. This was a practice match for the Newcastle Rangers club, which was formed in 1878. When the club folded, the West End Football Club took up residence at St. James' Park in 1886. When West End FC and Newcastle East End merged into Newcastle United in 1892, the new club moved into the venue for its home games and has been there ever since.

6. The stadium underwent its first major renovation in 1899, resulting in a capacity of 30,000 fans. In 1905, the capacity was then doubled to 60,000 and a swimming pool was added. The first game played at the venue under floodlights took place in February 1953 when Glasgow Celtic visited. This was three years before the English Football League played its first game under lights, which came in February 1956 at Fratton Park in Portsmouth with Newcastle the visitors. The record attendance at St. James' Park is 68,386 in a First Division match against Chelsea on September 3, 1930.

7. Newcastle has a long-standing and fierce rivalry with nearby club Sunderland. Games between these two teams

have been known as the Tyne-Wear Derby since 1898. Before each home contest, the team runs onto the pitch at home to the song "Local Hero" while fans often sing "Blaydon Races" during matches.

8. On-pitch fights between two soccer players are quite rare, as you're more likely to see the odd brawl involving several players. Even then, most skirmishes resemble elderly women swatting each other with their handbags. But in April 2005, fans at St. James' Park witnessed two players actually throwing and connecting with punches in anger during a match between Newcastle and Aston Villa. The problem was, both combatants belonged to the home side as Kieron Dyer and Lee Bowyer decided to slug it out after Bowyer reportedly accused teammate Dyer of not passing the ball to him. This resulted in straight red cards to both players while Villa waltzed to a 3-0 victory.

9. Goalkeeper Eddie Edgar was born in Jarrow, near Newcastle, and spent 1974 to 1976 with the club. He appeared in just one senior Newcastle match, a 4-2 loss to Derby County in the 1975-76 FA Cup quarterfinals. He then joined Fourth Division Hartlepool United and played 75 games. Edgar was loaned to the New York Cosmos in America, where he played with Pelé and backed up Shep Messing. He joined London City in Canada in 1980 and converted himself into a high-scoring center-forward. Edgar later coached university soccer and managed London City. Eddie's son David later played for

the Magpies and became a Canadian international defender.

10. These were the most-capped international players while members of Newcastle: Shay Given, Rep Ireland (80); Aaron Hughes, N Ireland (43); Nikos Dabizas, Greece (42); Alf McMichael, N Ireland (40); Gary Speed, Wales (36); Alan Shearer, England (35); Kieron Dyer, England (32); Nolberto Solano, Peru (29); David Craig, N Ireland (25); and Peter Beardsley, England (25).

CHAPTER 10:

DOMESTIC COMPETITION

QUIZ TIME!

1. How many league titles in all divisions has Newcastle won as of 2020?

    a. 4
    b. 8
    c. 9
    d. 6

2. Newcastle's first major trophy was the 1904-05 First Division league title.

    a. True
    b. False

3. Newcastle defeated which club to win its first FA Charity Shield?

    a. Queens Park Rangers
    b. Northampton Town
    c. Manchester United
    d. Tottenham Hotspur

4. What was the only year in which the club won the Sheriff of London Charity Shield Trophy?

   a. 1898
   b. 1900
   c. 1904
   d. 1907

5. Which club did the Magpies face in the 1950-51 FA Cup final?

   a. Sunderland AFC
   b. Birmingham City FC
   c. Wolverhampton Wanderers
   d. Blackpool FC

6. Newcastle faced which side in the 1904-05 FA Cup final?

   a. Everton FC
   b. Nottingham Forest
   c. Aston Villa
   d. Sheffield United

7. Newcastle was the first side to win the FA Charity Shield.

   a. True
   b. False

8. Which team did Newcastle face in the 1975-76 League Cup final?

   a. Leeds United
   b. Nottingham Forest
   c. Manchester City
   d. Liverpool FC

9. Which player scored the game-winning goal in the 1951 FA Cup final?

    a. Ted Robledo
    b. Jackie Milburn
    c. George Robledo
    d. Billy Foulkes

10. How many times has Newcastle won the FA Cup as of 2020?

    a. 8
    b. 6
    c. 3
    d. 2

11. Which squad eliminated Newcastle in the 1974-75 League Cup quarterfinal?

    a. Colchester United
    b. Aston Villa
    c. Ipswich Town
    d. Chester City FC

12. The Magpies have won the second-tier Second Division/Championship League six times as of 2020.

    a. True
    b. False

13. How many times has Newcastle won the First Division/ Premier League as of 2020?

    a. 8
    b. 7

c. 4

d. 2

14. Who scored the winner in the 1924 FA Cup final?

    a. James Low

    b. Tommy McDonald

    c. Neil Harris

    d. Billy Cowan

15. How many points did Newcastle post to win the 1926-27 First Division?

    a. 48

    b. 51

    c. 55

    d. 67

16. Newcastle has won a total of 18 major English trophies as of 2020.

    a. True

    b. False

17. Which side did the club face in the 1998 FA Cup final?

    a. Manchester United

    b. Arsenal FC

    c. Chelsea FC

    d. Sunderland AFC

18. How many times has Newcastle been runner-up in the FA Cup final?

    a. 10

    b. 7

c. 5

d. 3

19. The Magpies faced which team for the 1955 FA Charity Shield?

    a. Southampton FC

    b. Leeds United

    c. Tottenham Hotspur

    d. Chelsea FC

20. Newcastle won the 1943-44 Football League War Cup.

    a. True

    b. False

QUIZ ANSWERS

1. B – 8

2. A – True

3. B – Northampton Town

4. D – 1907

5. D – Blackpool FC

6. C – Aston Villa

7. A – True

8. C – Manchester City

9. C – George Robledo

10. B – 6

11. D – Chester City FC

12. B – False

13. C – 4

14. C – Neil Harris

15. D – 67

16. B – False

17. A – Manchester United

18. B – 7

19. D – Chelsea FC

20. B – False

DID YOU KNOW?

1. Newcastle has won four top-flight league titles and four second-tier championships. The side has also captured six FA Cup titles and one FA Charity/Community Shield but has yet to hoist the English League Cup as of 2020. The club has also been relegated six times.

2. The club captured its four top-flight titles in 1904-05, 1906-07, 1908-09, and 1926-27 in the First Division and was runner-up in the Premier League in 1995-96 and 1996-97. The second-tier titles were won in the First Division in 1992-93 and the Football League Championship Division in 2009-10 and 2016-17. The team also won the Second Division in 1964-65.

3. The FA Cup was hoisted by the team in 1909-10 versus Barnsley, 1923-24 versus Aston Villa, 1931-32 versus Arsenal, 1950-51 versus Blackpool, 1951-52 versus Arsenal, and 1954-55 versus Manchester City. The side also finished as FA Cup runner-up in 1904-05 versus Aston Villa, 1905-06 versus Everton, 1907-08 versus Wolverhampton Wanderers, 1910-11 versus Bradford City, 1973-74 versus Liverpool, 1997-98 versus Arsenal, and 1998-99 versus Manchester United.

4. Newcastle has made just one League Cup final, in 1975-76, when they were beaten 2-1 by Manchester City in front of 100,000 fans at Wembley Stadium. The club won the FA

Charity/Community Shield in 1909 versus Northampton Town and finished as runner-up in 1932, 1951, 1952, 1955, and 1996.

5. The club was relegated in 1933-34, 1960-61, 1977-78, and 1988-89 when it went from the top-flight First Division to the Second Division. It was also relegated from the top-flight Premier League to the second-tier Championship League division in 2008-09 and 2015-16.

6. Newcastle's record victory came in the Second Division on October 5, 1946, when they trounced Newport County 13-0 at home. Their biggest defeat was a 9-0 thrashing away to Burton Wanderers in the Second Division on April 15, 1895. The most league points accumulated in a campaign when two points were given for a win was 45 in the second-tier Second Division in 1964-65. The most points taken with three points given for a victory is 96 in the second-tier First Division in 1992-93. The most goals scored in a season was 98 in the top-flight First Division in 1951-52.

7. The top six individual seasons for scoring in all competitions for the club are 41 goals in 45 games by Andy Cole in 1993-94, 39 goals in 41 games by Hughie Gallacher in 1926-27, 39 goals in 46 games by George Robledo in 1951-52, 34 goals in 44 games by Hughie Gallacher in 1929-30, 34 goals in 53 games by Mick Quinn in 1989-90, and 34 goals in 46 games by Charlie Wayman in 1946-47. The most goals scored in a game was six by

Len Shackleton at home versus Newport County on October 5, 1946, in a 13-0 win.

8. The following players won the PFA Players' Player of the Year award while playing for the club: 1996, Les Ferdinand, and 1997, Alan Shearer. In addition, the following were named the PFA Young Player of the Year while members of Newcastle United: 1988, Paul Gascoigne; 1994, Andy Cole; 2002, Craig Bellamy; and 2003, Jermaine Jenas.

9. The 10 players who made the most domestic league appearances for the club are: 432, Jimmy Lawrence (1904-22); 430, Frank Hudspeth (1910-29); 402, Alf McMichael (1949-63); 389, Frank Clark (1962-75); 377, Bill McCracken (1904-23); 367, Bobby Mitchell (1949-61); 353, Jackie Milburn (1946-57); 351, David Craig (1962-78); 341, Tom McDonald (1921-31), and 336, Shay Given (1997-2009).

10. When Hereford United hosted Newcastle on their muddy pitch on February 5, 1972, they had already upset the Magpies by drawing 2-2 at St. James' Park in the third-round FA tie. The non-league club had a second chance to eliminate the First Division team in the replay. The Edgar Street Stadium held just 5,000 fans but 9,000 showed up. Their hopes were dashed, however, when Malcolm McDonald gave Newcastle the lead with just eight minutes remaining. Hereford equalized just three minutes later, and substitute Ricky George put them ahead 2-1 after 13 minutes of extra time. The pitch was invaded for a

second time as Hereford became the first non-league squad to down a First Division side in 23 years.

CHAPTER 11:

EUROPE & BEYOND

QUIZ TIME!

1. How many European Cup/Champions League trophies has Newcastle won as of 2020?

   a. 0

   b. 1

   c. 5

   d. 3

2. Newcastle reached the semifinals of the 2013-14 UEFA Europa League.

   a. True

   b. False

3. What was the first international trophy that Newcastle competed for?

   a. UEFA Euro Cup

   b. Anglo-Italian Cup

   c. UEFA Champions League

   d. European (Inter-Cities) Fairs Cup

4. How many matches has Newcastle played in the UEFA Champions League as of 2020?

   a. 15
   b. 34
   c. 19
   d. 24

5. Which club did Newcastle defeat to win the 1973-74 Texaco Cup?

   a. Burnley FC
   b. Norwich City FC
   c. Dundee United
   d. Leicester City FC

6. Which year did Newcastle win the Anglo-Italian Cup?

   a. 1968
   b. 1971
   c. 1973
   d. 1977

7. Newcastle has won the Europa League twice.

   a. True
   b. False

8. How many games has Newcastle played in the UEFA Europa Cup as of 2020?

   a. 72
   b. 65
   c. 48
   d. 32

9. Which team eliminated Newcastle in the 1998-99 UEFA Cup Winners' Cup?

    a. MSV Duisburg
    b. SC Braga
    c. FC Lausanne-Sport
    d. FK Partizan

10. Newcastle defeated which side in the 1968-69 European (Inter-Cities) Fairs Cup?

    a. Union Luxembourg
    b. Újpesti Dózsa FC
    c. Leeds United
    d. Real Madrid

11. Which club did the Magpies face in the 2001-02 Intertoto Cup final?

    a. AS Monaco FC
    b. Juventus
    c. TSV 1860 Munich
    d. Troyes FC

12. Alan Shearer is the club's record goal-scorer in international competitions.

    a. True
    b. False

13. How many times did Newcastle win the Texaco Cup?

    a. 6
    b. 4
    c. 2
    d. 1

14. Which club did Newcastle NOT face on the way to the 1968-69 European (Inter-Cities) Fairs Cup final?

   a. Göztepe SK
   b. Real Zaragoza
   c. Sporting CP
   d. Rangers FC

15. How many European (Inter-Cities) Fairs Cup games has Newcastle won?

   a. 16
   b. 13
   c. 10
   d. 8

16. The Magpies' first competitive international match was against Dutch club Feyenoord.

   a. True
   b. False

17. Newcastle defeated which side in the 1973 Anglo-Italian Cup final?

   a. Como 1907
   b. AS Roma
   c. AFC Fiorentina
   d. Bologna FC

18. How many goals did Alan Shearer score in international competitions for Newcastle?

   a. 18
   b. 24

c. 30

d. 36

19. Which squad eliminated Newcastle in the 2003-04 UEFA Euro Cup quarterfinals?

   a. Bayer Leverkusen

   b. RCD Mallorca

   c. PSV Eindhoven

   d. Olympique Marseille

20. Newcastle has played fewer than 100 competitive international matches as of 2020.

   a. True

   b. False

QUIZ ANSWERS

1. A – 0

2. B – False

3. D – European (Inter-Cities) Fairs Cup

4. D – 24

5. A – Burnley FC

6. C – 1973

7. B – False

8. A – 72

9. D – FK Partizan

10. B – Újpesti Dózsa FC

11. D – Troyes FC

12. A – True

13. C – 2

14. A – Göztepe SK

15. B – 13

16. A – True

17. C – AFC Fiorentina

18. C – 30

19. D – Olympique Marseille

20. B – False

DID YOU KNOW?

1. Newcastle's first venture into Europe was 1968-69 European (Inter-Cities) Fairs Cup, and its first appearance in the European Cup/Champions League was in 1997-98. Their only appearance in the Cup Winners' Cup came in 1998-99. Alan Shearer is the side's leading scorer in Europe, with 30 goals, while goalkeeper Shay Given has made the most appearances at 54.

2. The team played in the European (Inter-Cities) Fairs Cup three times, in 1968-69, 1969-70, and 1970-71; in the UEFA Cup/Europa League eight times, in 1977-78, 1994-95, 1996-97, 1999-2000, 2003-04, 2004-05, 2006-07, and 2012-13; in the European Champions League twice, in 1997-98 and 2002-03; in one UEFA Cup Winners' Cup, in 1998-99; and in the Intertoto Cup three times, in 2001-02, 2005-06, and 2006-07.

3. The only major competition Newcastle has won in Europe as of 2020 was the European (Inter-Cities) Fairs Cup tournament, where they beat Újpest Dózsa of Hungary in 1968-69. This competition was also known as the Inter-Cities Fairs Cup, the Fairs Cities' Cup, and the Fairs Cup. The competition ran from 1955 to 1971 as the forerunner to the UEFA Cup, which then became the UEFA Europa League.

4. In the 1968-69 European (Inter-Cities) Fairs Cup, Newcastle beat Újpesti Dózsa 6-2 on aggregate in the final by winning the first leg 3-0 at home and the second leg 3-2 in Hungary. The club beat Feyenoord of Holland 4-2 on aggregate in the first round, Sporting Lisbon of Portugal 2-1 on aggregate in the second round, were level 4-4 with Real Zaragoza in the third round and advanced on the away-goals rule, beat Vitória de Setúbal of Portugal 6-4 on aggregate in the quarterfinals, and downed Glasgow Rangers 2-0 on aggregate in the semifinals.

5. Newcastle also had success in the complicated Intertoto Cup competition in 2005-06. The event was founded in 1961-62 but didn't become an official UEFA tournament until 1995. The competition initially had a single champion, but, starting in 1967, it ended with several group winners who received cash prizes. When the UEFA got involved, it became a qualifying event for the UEFA Cup, with group winners advancing to the second qualifying round of the UEFA Cup. Newcastle was one of 11 group winners in 2006.

6. As of 2020-21, Newcastle's record in the European Champions League was 11 wins, three draws, and 10 losses with an even goal differential for a winning percentage of 45.83. Their mark in the UEFA Cup/Europa League was 42 wins, 17 draws, and 13 defeats with a +63 goal difference for a 58.33 winning percentage. Their record in the UEFA Cup Winners' Cup was a win and loss with an even goal difference for a winning percentage

113

of 50.00. The club's record in the European (Inter-Cities) Fairs Cup was 13 victories, six draws, and five losses with a +16 goal difference for a 54.17 winning percentage. Their overall record in these major competitions currently stands at 67 wins, 26 draws, and 29 losses with a +79 goal difference for a 54.92 winning percentage.

7. Newcastle did manage to win two trophies in the minor European competition known as the Texaco Cup/Anglo-Scottish Cup. This was an association competition involving league sides from England, Scotland, and Ireland that hadn't qualified for a major European tournament. However, the Irish and Northern Irish clubs withdrew from the event after 1971-72 because of political pressure and competed in the All-Ireland Cup in 1973-74 and 1974-75. The event was then called the Anglo-Scottish Cup from 1975-76 to 1980-81. Newcastle beat Burnley 2-1 on aggregate to win the 1973-74 final and downed Southampton 3-1 on aggregate in the 1974-75 final.

8. Success was also reached in another minor European tournament known as the Anglo-Italian Cup (Coppa Anglo-Italiana), which was also known as the Anglo-Italian Inter-League Clubs Competition, the Alitalia Challenge Cup, the Talbot Challenge Cup, and the Gigi Peronace Memorial. This event ran from time to time between 1970 and 1996 for teams from England and Italy. Newcastle edged Fiorentina of Italy 2-1 in the 1973 final.

9. The club's top 10 scorers in major European competitions are: 30, Alan Shearer; 12, Shola Ameobi; 11, Craig

114

Bellamy; 10, Wyn Davies; 9, Bryan Robson; 9, Faustino Asprilla; 7, Nolberto Solano; 5, Jimmy Scott; 5, Gary Speed; 5, Patrick Kluivert; and 5, Laurent Robert.

10. Players who made the most appearances in major European matches for Newcastle are: 54, Shay Given; 49, Alan Shearer; 44, Aaron Hughes; 39, Gary Speed; 37, Shola Ameobi; 37, Andy O'Brien; 35, Laurent Robert; 32, Olivier Bernard; 32, Jermaine Jenas; and 31, Nolberto Solano.

CHAPTER 12:

TOP SCORERS

QUIZ TIME!

1. Who was the first player to lead Newcastle in league scoring in the Second Division?

   a. Robert Willis
   b. Willie Thompson
   c. Thomas Crate
   d. Joseph Wallace

2. Alan Shearer won three consecutive Golden Boot awards with Newcastle between 1996-97 and 1999-2000.

   a. True
   b. False

3. How many players have led the First Division/Premier League in goals with Newcastle?

   a. 4
   b. 5
   c. 7
   d. 10

4. Who won the 1993-94 Premier League Golden Boot?

    a. Andy Cole
    b. Peter Beardsley
    c. Ruel Fox
    d. Paul Kitson

5. Which player holds the club record for most goals scored in all competitions as of 2020?

    a. Hughie Gallacher
    b. Len White
    c. Alan Shearer
    d. Jackie Milburn

6. Who led the team with 23 goals in the 2016-17 domestic league season?

    a. Daryl Murphy
    b. Christian Atsu
    c. Dwight Gayle
    d. Matt Ritchie

7. Albert Shepherd was the first Newcastle player to lead the First Division in scoring in 1910-11.

    a. True
    b. False

8. How many goals did Andy Cole tally in the 1993-94 Premier League?

    a. 22
    b. 26
    c. 29
    d. 34

9. Which two players led Newcastle with six goals each in the 2000-01 Premier League?

    a. Kevin Gallacher and James Coppinger

    b. Brian Kerr and Shola Ameobi

    c. Stephen Glass and Daniel Cordone

    d. Nolberto Solano and Carl Cort

10. Which player scored 32 domestic league goals in 1989-90?

    a. Mark McGhee

    b. Micky Quinn

    c. Gary Brazil

    d. John Anderson

11. How many goals did Albert Shepherd score in all competitions in 1910-11?

    a. 18

    b. 26

    c. 33

    d. 35

12. Jackie Milburn holds the Magpies' record for most goals scored in a domestic league season, with 37.

    a. True

    b. False

13. How many goals did Andy Carroll net in the 2009-10 Championship League?

    a. 17

    b. 12

    c. 20

    d. 8

14. Who won the 1951-52 Golden Boot award?

    a. Bobby Mitchell
    b. Charlie Wayman
    c. Jackie Milburn
    d. George Robledo

15. How many goals did Jackie Milburn score in all competitions in his Newcastle career?

    a. 202
    b. 200
    c. 196
    d. 187

16. Andy Cole holds the club record for most goals scored in a season in all competitions, with 45.

    a. True
    b. False

17. Who led Newcastle with 12 goals in the 2010-11 Premier League?

    a. Ryan Donaldson
    b. Alan Smith
    c. Kevin Nolan
    d. Nile Ranger

18. How many goals did Alan Shearer score in all competitions with Newcastle?

    a. 193
    b. 200
    c. 206
    d. 210

19. Which player led the First Division with 21 goals in 1974-75?

    a. Pat Howard
    b. Alan Kennedy
    c. John Tudor
    d. Malcolm Macdonald

20. Hughie Gallacher scored 143 goals in 174 appearances in all competitions.

    a. True
    b. False

QUIZ ANSWERS

1. D – Joseph Wallace

2. B – False

3. B – 5

4. A – Andy Cole

5. C – Alan Shearer

6. C – Dwight Gayle

7. A – True

8. D – 34

9. D – Nolberto Solano and Carl Cort

10. B – Micky Quinn

11. C – 33

12. B – False

13. A – 17

14. D – George Robledo

15. B – 200

16. B – False

17. C – Kevin Nolan

18. C – 206

19. D – Malcolm Macdonald

20. A – True

DID YOU KNOW?

1. Former Newcastle captain, manager, and England international striker Alan Shearer is the club's all-time top scorer with 206 goals in 404 games. He's also the Premier League's top scorer with 261 goals in 441 outings, and he tallied 30 times in 63 matches for his country. He joined from Blackburn Rovers in 1996 for a then world-record £18.9 million after being named the Football Writers' Association Player of the Year in 1994 and the PFA Player of the Year in 1995. He helped Blackburn win the Premier League in 1994-95, and he won two Golden Boots there. Shearer played 10 years with Newcastle and led his hometown team to the 1998 and 1999 FA Cup finals, winning a Golden Boot in 1996-97. The English and Newcastle Football Hall of Fame member holds numerous club and Premier League scoring records and milestones.

2. English international forward Jackie Milburn began his pro career with the Magpies, from 1946 to 1957, and netted 200 goals in 397 outings while scoring 10 in 13 games with England. Nicknamed "Wor Jackie," Milburn was related to Jack and Bobby Charlton. He scored twice in the 1950-51 FA Cup final triumph and netted a goal after just 45 seconds in the 1954-55 final to help win it again. He also won the trophy in 1951-52. Milburn held the club scoring record from 1957 to February 2006 when

Alan Shearer broke it. A statue of Milburn, who's a member of the English Football Hall of Fame, now sits just outside St. James' Park.

3. Len White joined from Rotherham in 1952-53 and remained until joining Huddersfield Town a decade later. The forward cost £12,500 and typically played up front alongside Jackie Milburn during the 1950s. He helped the squad capture the 1954-55 FA Cup and finished his Newcastle career as the team's third-highest scorer with 153 markers in 269 appearances. His brother Jack White also played professional soccer with Aldershot and Bristol City before turning to management.

4. When it comes to goals per game, it's hard to top Hughie Gallacher, who netted 143 goals for the Magpies in 174 matches for an average of .82 goals an outing. The Scottish international also notched 24 goals in 20 appearances for his country. He joined from Airdrieonians in 1925 after scoring 100 goals in 129 games for them. Gallacher scored twice in his Newcastle debut and led the club with 23 league goals in 19 contests in his first season even though he arrived just before Christmas. He was made team captain and helped the side win the First Division in 1926-27 and set a club record with 36 league goals in 38 appearances. Gallacher joined Chelsea in 1930.

5. English international forward Malcolm Macdonald joined for £180,000 from Luton Town in the summer of 1971 and promptly scored a hat-trick in his home debut against

Liverpool, thus earning the nickname "Supermac." He posted 30 goals in 52 games in his first campaign to lead the team and went on to lead the squad in scoring for the next four seasons. He captured the First Division Golden Boot in 1975-76 with 19 goals in 39 games. Macdonald scored twice against Burnley in the 1973-74 FA Cup semifinal to lead the side to the final, but they were beaten 3-0 by Liverpool. He joined Arsenal in 1976 for the odd fee of £333,333.34 and won a Golden Boot there in 1976-77.

6. Peter Beardsley, who was effective as both a midfielder and forward due to his sublime skills, had two stints with his hometown club. He played briefly with Manchester United before joining the Vancouver Whitecaps in Canada, and he came to Newcastle in 1983, helping the side earn promotion to the top flight. The English international, known as "Little Gem," joined Liverpool in 1987 and made a stop in Everton before returning to the Magpies in 1993 for four more years. Beardsley notched 119 goals in 326 appearances. He later became a coach with the club and managed it briefly as a caretaker.

7. After serving in the Royal Horse Artillery during the First World War, forward Tom McDonald of Scotland played for Newcastle from 1921 to 1931 after joining from Glasgow Rangers and before leaving for York City. The 5-foot-8 McDonald scored 113 times in 367 matches with the Magpies and helped them win the FA Cup in 1923-24 and the First Division crown in 1926-27. McDonald eventually

hung up his boots in 1934 after finishing his career with a semi-pro English outfit named Goole Town.

8. Also scoring 113 goals for Newcastle was Scottish international Bobby Mitchell, who did it in 410 games. He arrived from Third Lanark in Glasgow for a reported £16,000 in February 1949 and stayed until leaving for Berwick Rangers in 1961. Mitchell was a hero to Magpies supporters, who nicknamed him "Dazzler." He was an integral part of the team and helped it win FA Cups in 1950-51, 1951-52, and 1954-55. He scored in the 1955 final. After hanging up his boots, he ran a pub in Newcastle. He played twice for the Scottish national team and scored on his debut.

9. Forward Neil Harris played with several teams in his homeland of Scotland for seven years before arriving at Newcastle in May 1920 for £3,300. He appeared in 194 games for the team and contributed 101 goals, with 14 of those coming in FA Cup encounters and the other 87 coming in the league. He scored the opening goal of the 1923-24 FA Cup final, which Newcastle won, and then left for Notts County in November 1925 for a fee of £3,000. Harris later managed teams in England, Scotland, and Wales.

10. With 97 goals in 244 outings, center-forward Bryan "Pop" Robson was ranked 10th on the club's all-time scoring list as of March 2021. He kicked off his pro career with Newcastle from 1962 to 1971 before joining West Ham

United. He helped the side win the Second Division championship in 1964-65 and the European (Inter-Cities) Fairs Cup in 1968-69. When Robson was sold to West Ham in February 1971, he became that club's record transfer purchase at the time at £120,000.

CONCLUSION

Newcastle United is well into its second century of existence now, and you've just read about the first 120 years or so of the lengthy journey. We've served it up in a lighthearted and fun manner while still trying to provide you with educational and noteworthy facts about the club.

We've touched on the team's records, milestones, transfers, triumphs, and tribulations regarding their performances in the UK and on the European continent, as well.

With such a lengthy history to wade through, it's impossible to include each and every member of the club, and we hope we haven't had to leave out too many of your favorites.

We've filled the previous pages with 12 different chapters, with each chapter offering a challenging trivia quiz. In addition, all dozen chapters featured a wide range of "Did You Know?" facts.

By taking the quizzes and processing all of the facts, you should now be ready, willing, and able to take on the toughest Newcastle United quiz challenges you come across.

We also hope you'll be inclined to share this Newcastle trivia book with fellow Toon Army members or supporters of other clubs to help share the side's marvelous history.

While the club continues to compete as hard as it possibly can from season to season, its passionate fans continue to exhibit their loyalty to the side.

Thank you for being one of those amazing Newcastle supporters and for taking the time to celebrate the club's history by reading our latest trivia and fact offering. It's greatly appreciated.

Printed in Great Britain
by Amazon

35175049R00076